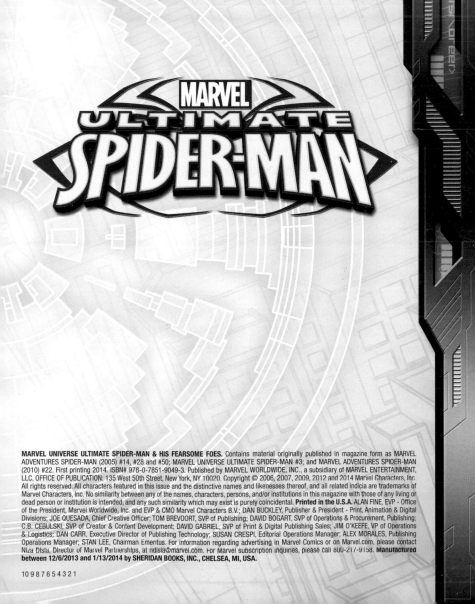

MARVEL UNIVERSE ULTIMATE SPIDER-MAN & HIS FEARSOME FOES. Contains material originally published in magazine form as MARVEL ADVENTURES SPIDER-MAN (2005) #14, #28 and #50; MARVEL UNIVERSE ULTIMATE SPIDER-MAN #3; and MARVEL ADVENTURES SPIDER-MAN (2010) #22. First printing 2014. ISBN# 978-0-7851-9049-3. Published by MARVEL WORLDWIDE, INC., a subsidiary of MARVEL ENTERTAINMENT, LLC. OFFICE OF PUBLICATION: 135 West 50th Street, New York, NY 10020. Copyright © 2006, 2007, 2009, 2012 and 2014 Marvel Characters, Inc. All rights reserved. All characters featured in this issue and the distinctive names and likenesses thereof, and all related indicia are trademarks of Marvel Characters, Inc. No similarity between any of the names, characters, persons, and/or institutions in this magazine with those of any living or dead person or institution is intended, and any such similarity which may exist is purely coincidental. **Printed in the U.S.A.** ALAN FINE, EVP - Office of the President, Marvel Worldwide, Inc. and EVP & CMO Marvel Characters B.V.; DAN BUCKLEY, Publisher & President - Print, Animation & Digital Divisions; JOE QUESADA, Chief Creative Officer; TOM BREVOORT, SVP of Publishing; DAVID BOGART, SVP of Operations & Procurement, Publishing; C.B. CEBULSKI, SVP of Creator & Content Development; DAVID GABRIEL, SVP of Print & Digital Publishing Sales; JIM O'KEEFE, VP of Operations & Logistics; DAN CARR, Executive Director of Publishing Technology; SUSAN CRESPI, Editorial Operations Manager; ALEX MORALES, Publishing Operations Manager; STAN LEE, Chairman Emeritus. For information regarding advertising in Marvel Comics or on Marvel.com, please contact Niza Disla, Director of Marvel Partnerships, at ndisla@marvel.com. For Marvel subscription inquiries, please call 800-217-9158. **Manufactured between 12/6/2013 and 1/13/2014 by SHERIDAN BOOKS, INC., CHELSEA, MI, USA.**

10 9 8 7 6 5 4 3 2 1

MARVEL
ULTIMATE SPIDER-MAN

"THAT'S ALL FOLKS"
WRITER: **JAKE SEMAHN**
ARTIST: **TY TEMPLETON**
COLOR ARTIST: **WIL QUINTANA**
LETTERER: **VC'S JOE CARAMAGNA**
ASSISTANT EDITOR: **ELLIE PYLE**
ASSOCIATE EDITOR: **TOM BRENNAN**
SENIOR EDITOR: **STEPHEN WACKER**

"THE BLACK CAT?!"
WRITER: **ZEB WELLS**
PENCILER: **PATRICK SCHERBERGER**
INKS: **NORMAN LEE**
COLORIST: **GURU e-FX**
LETTERER: **DAVE SHARPE**
COVER ARTISTS: **AMANDA CONNOR,
JIMMY PALMIOTTI & CHRIS SOTOMAYOR**
ASSISTANT EDITOR: **NATHAN COSBY**
EDITOR: **MACKENZIE CADENHEAD**
CONSULTING EDITOR: **MARK PANICCIA**

"I-- HATE-- SPIDER-MAN!"
WRITER: **CHRIS KIPINIAK**
PENCILER: **PATRICK SCHERBERGER**
INKERS: **NORMAN LEE & ROLAND PARIS**
COLORIST: **GURU e-FX**
LETTERER: **DAVE SHARPE**
COVER ARTISTS: **PATRICK SCHERBERGER,
ROLAND PARIS & GURU e-FX**
ASSISTANT EDITOR: **NATHAN COSBY**
EDITOR: **MARK PANICCIA**

"SINISTER SIX(TEENTH)"
WRITER: **MARC SUMERAK**
PENCILER: **SANFORD GREENE**
INKER: **NATHAN MASSENGILL**
COLORIST: **SOTOCOLOR'S A. STREET**
LETTERER: **DAVE SHARPE**
COVER ARTISTS: **PATRICK SCHERBERGER & NEI RUFFINO**
EDITOR: **NATHAN COSBY**
CONSULTING EDITOR: **RALPH MACCHIO**

"DUMB LUCK!"
WRITER: **PAUL TOBIN**
ARTIST: **TODD NAUCK**
COLOR ARTIST: **CHRIS SOTOMAYOR**
LETTERER: **DAVE SHARPE**
COVER ARTISTS: **ALE GARZA & CHRIS SOTOMAYOR**
EDITOR: **TOM BRENNAN**
SENIOR EDITOR: **STEPHEN WACKER**

Collection Editor: **Cory Levine**
Assistant Editors: **Alex Starbuck & Nelson Ribeiro**
Editors, Special Projects: **Jennifer Grünwald & Mark D. Beazley**
Senior Editor, Special Projects: **Jeff Youngquist**
SVP of Print & Digital Publishing Sales: **David Gabriel**

Editor In Chief: **Axel Alonso**
Chief Creative Officer: **Joe Quesada**
Publisher: **Dan Buckley**
Executive Producer: **Alan Fine**

WHILE ATTENDING A DEMONSTRATION IN RADIOLOGY, HIGH SCHOOL STUDENT PETER PARKER WAS BITTEN BY A SPIDER THAT HAD ACCIDENTALLY BEEN EXPOSED TO RADIOACTIVE RAYS. THROUGH A MIRACLE OF SCIENCE, PETER SOON FOUND THAT HE HAD GAINED THE SPIDER'S POWERS...AND HAD, IN EFFECT, BECOME A HUMAN SPIDER! FROM THAT DAY ON, HE HAS ENDEAVORED TO BECOME THE...

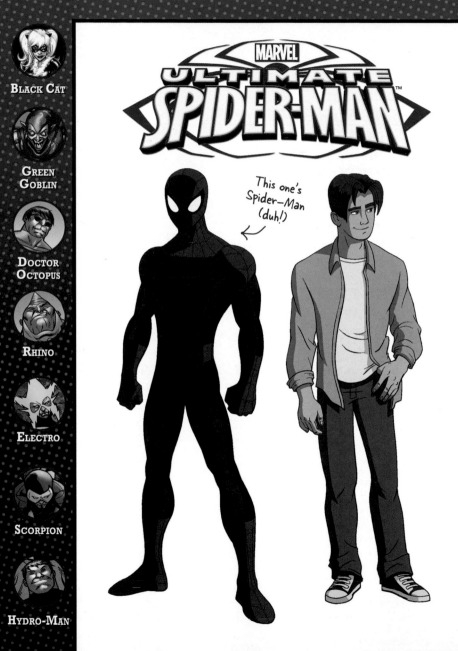

THAT'S ALL FOLKS!

WRITTEN BY JAKE SEMAHN   ART BY TY TEMPLETON   COLOR ART BY WIL QUINTANA   LETTERS BY VC'S JOE CARAMAGNA
ASSISTANT EDITOR: ELLIE PYLE   ASSOCIATE EDITOR: TOM BRENNAN   SENIOR EDITOR: STEPHEN WACKER
ALONSO, QUESADA, LOEB, BUCKLEY, FINE — HEAD HONCHOS

ZEB WELLS
WRITER
DAVE SHARPE
LETTERER

PATRICK SCHERBERGER
PENCILS
BRAD JOHANSEN
PRODUCTION

NORMAN LEE
INKS

NATHAN COSBY
ASST. EDITOR

MACKENZIE CADENHEAD
EDITOR

GURU eFX
COLORS

MARK PANICCIA
CONSULTING EDITOR

AMANDA CONNER with PALMIOTTI and SOTO
COVER

JOE QUESADA
CHIEF

DAN BUCKLEY
PUBLISHER

Whew! Took me a while to get out of there...hope Aunt May isn't worried.

Peter! Is that you?! Where have you been?!

I... uh...

Oh, never mind! Liz Allen just called and wants to know why you haven't picked her up for the big dance!

Oh! O-okay...

Ha! I knew Liz wouldn't ditch me to go with Flash! And I'm supposed to believe in *bad luck?!* Bah!

Although, I'm sure there's *someone* out there who would beg to differ right about now.

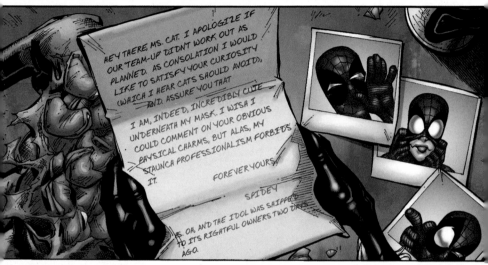

BITTEN BY AN IRRADIATED SPIDER, WHICH GRANTED HIM INCREDIBLE ABILITIES, **PETER PARKER** LEARNED THE ALL-IMPORTANT LESSON, THAT WITH GREAT POWER THERE MUST ALSO COME GREAT RESPONSIBILITY. AND SO HE BECAME THE AMAZING **SPIDER-MAN!**

Hey, you! Kid!

I know why you bought this comic. You're a fan of that pesky, wall-crawling itch, *Spider-Man*, aren't you?

I bet you think that, just because his name's on the cover, *Spider-Man's* just gonna waltz in, save the day, and come back for another tale next month. Am I right?

Well, I've got some bad news for you...not this time.

Enjoy the *Spider-Man* story, small-fry. I'm going to make sure it's his *last*, because...

I-- HATE-- SPIDER- MAN!

MARVEL Adventures SPIDER-MAN

CHRIS KIPINIAK
WRITER

PATRICK SCHERBERGER
PENCILER

NORMAN LEE & ROLAND PARIS
INKERS

GURU eFX
COLORISTS

DAVE SHARPE
LETTERER

SCHERBERGER, PARIS et GURU eFX
COVER

RICH GINTER
PRODUCTION

NATHAN COSBY
ASSISTANT EDITOR

MARK PANICCIA
EDITOR

JOE QUESADA
EDITOR IN CHIEF

DAN BUCKLEY
PUBLISHER

The following week...

What can I say? We was wrong.

We heard what you did to Spider-Man. Everyone knows. And everyone's scared.

We're hoping you ain't mad at us.

I need muscle too much to be mad. You're in. You're lucky business is expanding so quickly.

But there's still much to do. So many haven't learned the lesson you have.

It's time to teach them.

A few days later...
(Yeesh! Time flies, doesn't it?)

I don't know what I'm looking at.

Laundromat? Baseball stadium? Dog pound?

Oh, no! Don't go so soon! We're just getting started!

--hide?

Oh, that's disappointing! You came for a fight, didn't you? Now you're *hiding*?!

You can run, Spider-Man, but you can't--

Show yourself! Are you scared? Like the rest of them? Scared of the *GREEN GOBLIN*?!

When you throw a *birthday party*, it's not unusual to end up with a few *uninvited guests*.

But when you're *Peter Parker*-- the Amazing *Spider-Man*--those *party crashers* never show up to *eat cake* or *give presents*.

They only come for *one thing*:

Revenge.

DOCTOR OCTOPUS

ELECTRO

RHINO

GREEN GOBLIN

SCORPION

HYDRO-MAN

Make a *wish*, Spidey... that you'll *survive* to see another year!

SINISTER SIX-TEENTH

Marc Sumerak writer *Sanford Greene* penciler *Nathan Massengill* inker *Sotocolor's A. Street* colorist *Dave Sharpe* letterer *TOM V.C.* production *Patrick Scherberger* cover artist *Ralph Macchio* consulting *Nathan Cosby* editor *Joe Quesada* editor in chief *Dan Buckley* publisher *Alan Fine* Executive Producer

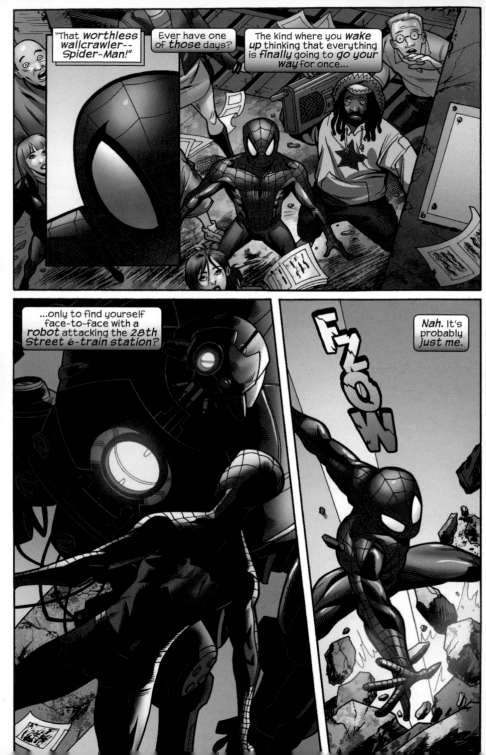

Gross.

I wish I had time to wring the *Hydro-Man* out of my *tights*...

...but if I wanna *stand a chance* against my *biggest baddies*, I've gotta *act quick*...

You're gonna *pay* for that!

THW

My *eyes!* NO fair!

...and hope these guys are still as *dumb* as I *remember*.

ELECTRO!

Power down, you fool!

The *water!*

You're going to--

THE END.